WEIGHT SMOOTHIE RECIPES

DR. NANCY GOLD

1 | WEIGHT GAIN SMOOTHIE RECIPE

TABLE OF CONTENT

INTRODUCTION

A smoothie is a beverage made by puréeing ingredients in a blender. A smoothie commonly has a liquid base, such as fruit juice or milk, yogurt, ice cream or cottage cheese. Other ingredients may be added, including fruits, vegetables, non-dairy milk, crushed ice, whey powder or nutritional supplements.

Nutrition

The nutrition of a smoothie depends on its ingredients and their proportions. Many smoothies include large or multiple servings of fruits and vegetables, which are recommended in a healthy diet and intended to be a meal replacement.

However, fruit juice containing high amounts of sugar can increase caloric intake and promote weight gain. Ingredients such as protein powders, sweeteners, or ice cream may be used. One study found smoothies to be less satiating, despite providing the same amount of energy as unblended foods.

Types of smoothies

Green smoothie

A green smoothie typically consists of 40–50% green vegetables (roughly half), usually raw green leafy vegetables, such as spinach, kale, Swiss chard, collard greens, celery, parsley, or broccoli, with the remaining ingredients being mostly or entirely fruit.

Most green leafy vegetables have a bitter flavor when served raw, but this can be ameliorated by choosing certain less-bitter vegetables (e.g. baby spinach) or combining with fruits or other sweet ingredients.

Protein smoothie

A protein smoothie is a combination of water or some form of dairy product, protein powder, fruits, and vegetables. They can be consumed any part of the day and are used as protein supplement for those who want to increase their protein intake. Protein powder can have a chalky taste when mixed individually by itself with milk or water.

The protein smoothie improves the taste of the protein powder through addition of fruits or other sweeteners.

WEIGHT GAIN

Weight gain is an increase in body weight. This can involve an increase in muscle mass, fat deposits, excess fluids such as water or other factors. Weight gain can be a symptom of a serious medical condition.

Description

Weight gain occurs when more energy (as calories from food and beverage consumption) is gained than the energy expended by life activities, including normal physiological processes and physical exercise.

If enough weight is gained due to increased body fat deposits, one may become overweight or obese, generally defined as having more body fat (adipose tissue) than is considered good for health. The Body Mass Index (BMI) measures body weight in proportion to height, and defines optimal, insufficient, and excessive weight based on the ratio.

Having excess adipose tissue (fat) is a common condition, especially where food supplies are plentiful and lifestyles are sedentary. Overweight and obesity may increase the risk of several diseases, such as diabetes, heart disease, and some cancers, and may lead to short- and long-term health problems during pregnancy.

Rates of obesity worldwide tripled from 1975 to 2016 to involve some 1.8 billion people and 39% of the world adult population.

The Wishnofsky Rule states that one pound of human fat tissue contains about 3,500 kilocalories (often simply called calories in the field of nutrition). Wishnofsky conducted a review of previous observations and experiments on weight loss and weight gain, and stated his conclusions in a paper he published in 1958.

Thus, according to the Wishnofsky Rule, eating 500 fewer calories than one needs per day should result in a loss of about a pound per week. Similarly, for every 3500 calories consumed above the amount one needs, a pound will be gained.

Wishnofsky noted that previous research suggested that a pound of human adipose tissue is 87% fat, which equals 395 grams of fat. He further assumed that animal fat contains 9.5 calories per gram. Thus one pound of human fat tissue should contain 3750 calories.

He then critically analyzed the relevant literature and applied a number of additional assumptions, including that the diet contains sufficient protein and that the person is in glycogen and nitrogen (protein) equilibrium, leading to most weight loss stemming from the catabolism of fat.

He concluded that a 3500-calorie excess or deficit for a person meeting his assumptions, would lead to the gain or loss, respectively, of one pound of body weight.

He noted that if the assumptions he made are not met, a deficit of 3500 calories would not necessarily equate to a pound of weight loss.

Wishnofsky did not take into account numerous aspects of human physiology and biochemistry which were unknown at the time. The claim has achieved the status of a rule of thumb and is repeated in numerous sources, used for diet planning by dietitians and misapplied at the population level as well.

Causes of weight gain

In regard to adipose tissue increases, a person generally gains weight by increasing food consumption, becoming physically inactive, or both.

When energy intake exceeds energy expenditure (when the body is in positive energy balance), the body can store the excess energy as fat. However, the physiology of weight gain and loss is complex involving numerous hormones, body systems and environmental factors. Other factors besides energy balance that may contribute to gaining weight include:

Social factors

A study, involving more than 12,000 people tracked over 32 years, found that social networks play a surprisingly powerful role in determining an individual's chances of gaining weight, transmitting an increased risk of becoming obese from wives to husbands, from brothers to brothers and from friends to friends.

The human microbiota facilitates fermentation of indigestible carbohydrates to short-chain fatty acids, SCFAs, contributing to weight gain. A change in the proportion of Bacteroidetes and Firmicutes may determine host's risk of obesity.

Sleep and stress

Lack of sufficient sleep has been suggested as a cause for weight gain or the difficulty in maintaining a healthy weight. Two hormones responsible for regulating hunger and metabolism are leptin, which inhibits appetite and increases energy expenditure, and ghrelin, which increases appetite and reduces energy expenditure. Studies have shown that chronic sleep deprivation is associated with reduced levels of leptin and elevated levels of ghrelin, which together result in increased appetite, especially for high fat and high carbohydrate foods.

As a result, sleep deprivation over time may contribute to increased caloric intake and decreased self-control over food cravings, leading to weight gain.

Hormone and neurotransmitter imbalances

Weight gain is a common side-effect of certain psychiatric medications.

Pathologies

Pathological causes of weight gain include Cushing's syndrome, hypothyroidism, insulinoma, and craniopharyngioma. Genetic reasons can relate to Prader–Willi syndrome, Bardet–Biedl syndrome, Alström syndrome, Cohen syndrome, and Carpenter syndrome.

HOW TO GAIN WEIGHT FAST:

TIPS TO BE SAFE AND HEALTHY

Which food is best for weight gain?

If you're underweight and looking to gain weight, it's very important to do it right.

Consuming soda, donuts, and other junk foods may help you gain weight initially, but it can increase your risk of heart disease, diabetes, and cancer.

A healthier approach to gaining weight involves gaining a balanced amount of muscle mass and subcutaneous fat rather than a lot of unhealthy belly fat.

A recent animal study suggests that belly fat specifically may be correlated with increased cancer risk.

A high percentage of body fat also increases your chances of developing type 2 diabetes and other health problems, even if you are not overweight.

To gain weight healthily, focus on eating more nutrient-dense foods and living an overall healthy lifestyle that involves exercising, getting enough sleep, and reducing stress, if you can.

This book outlines simple strategies to quickly gain weight without increasing your risk of disease.

Why is gaining weight important?

While about 74 percent of adults in the U.S. are either overweight or obese, there are also many people with the opposite problem of being underweight.

Some individuals may be naturally underweight due to genetics or a fast metabolism. Being underweight may also be indicative of poor nutrition or underlying health conditions.

Additionally, many people who are not clinically underweight may still want to gain some muscle and put on weight for other reasons.

Whether you're clinically underweight or simply struggling to gain muscle weight, the main principles are the same.

What does it mean to be 'underweight'?

Being underweight is defined as having a body mass index (BMI) below 18.5. This is estimated to be less than the body mass needed to sustain optimal health.

You can use this calculator to see where you fit on the BMI scale.

However, keep in mind that there are many problems with the BMI scale, which only looks at weight and height. It does not take muscle mass into account. Some people are naturally very skinny but still healthy. Being underweight according to this scale does not necessarily mean that you have a health problem.

According to the Centers for Disease Control and Prevention (CDC), being underweight is about twice as common among women, compared with men. In a U.S. survey that grouped participants into men and women, 1.3% of men and 2% of women 20 years and older are underweight.

Health risks linked to being underweight

Being underweight can be harmful to your health.

One study found that clinically underweight individuals have nearly two times the risk of death compared to obese individuals, suggesting that being underweight may be worse for your health than being obese.

Additionally, another study found that self-reported health outcomes fell significantly in underweight individuals after the age of 38, indicating that a low BMI later in life may come with increased health risks.

Being underweight can impair your immune function, raise your risk of infection, lead to osteoporosis and fractures and cause fertility problems.

What's more, people who are underweight are much more likely to get sarcopenia (age-related muscle wasting) and may be at greater risk of dementia.

For children, it can also lead to growth and development problems.

Causes of being underweight

There are several medical conditions that can cause unhealthy weight loss, including:

• Eating disorders: This includes anorexia nervosa, a serious mental health disorder.

• Thyroid problems: Having an overactive thyroid (hyperthyroidism) can boost metabolism and cause unhealthy weight loss.

• Celiac disease: The most severe form of gluten intolerance. Overall, the incidence of celiac disease has risen throughout the 20th and 21st centuries.

• Diabetes: Having uncontrolled diabetes (mainly type 1) can lead to severe weight loss.

• Cancer: Cancer can cause the body to be in a hypercatabolic state, which leads to increased energy being used. It can cause someone to lose a lot of weight but the severity and weight loss can depend on the type of cancer and the age of the person.

• Infections: Certain infections can cause someone to become severely underweight. This can include parasites, tuberculosis, and HIV infection.

If you're underweight, you may want to make an appointment with a doctor to rule out any serious medical conditions.

This is particularly important if you have recently started losing large amounts of weight without trying.

Different strategies for gaining weight

Whatever your reasons are for wanting to gain weight, there are a variety of strategies you can use to bulk up.

Below, we've outlined several different ways to help you gain weight.

Increase your caloric intake

The most important thing you can do to gain weight is to create a calorie surplus, meaning you eat more calories than your body needs.

You can determine your calorie needs using this calorie calculator.

If you want to gain weight slowly and steadily, aim for 300–500 calories more than you burn each day according to the calculator. If you want to gain weight fast, aim for around 700–1,000 calories above your maintenance level.

Keep in mind that calorie calculators only provide estimates. Your needs may vary by several hundred calories per day, give or take.

You don't need to count calories for the rest of your life, but it can help to do it for the first few days or weeks to get a feel for how many calories you're eating. There are many great tools out there to help you.

Increase your protein intake

Adequate consumption of high-quality proteins from animal products is essential for optimal growth, development, and human health.

To promote skeletal and muscle growth and physical strength in healthy adults with minimal to intense physical activity, the Recommended Dietary Allowance of protein is between 1.0 to 1.6 grams of protein per kilogram of body weight per day.

Up to 2 grams per kilogram of body weight of protein per day may be safe for healthy adults, with the upper limit at 3.5 grams per kilogram of body weight per day.

High protein foods include meats, fish, eggs, many dairy products, legumes, nuts, and others. Protein supplements like whey protein can also be useful it is difficult for you to get enough protein in your diet.

However, protein may also reduce your hunger and appetite significantly, making it harder to get in enough calories.

Additionally, eating too much protein may also increase your risk of heart disease. Talk with a doctor to see if increasing your protein intake would help you achieve your goal to gain weight in a safe way.

Increase your intake of carbs and fat

Many people try restricting either carbs or fat when trying to lose weight.

This may make it hard to gain weight, as it will make it harder to get in enough calories.

Eat plenty of high carb and high fat foods if weight gain is a priority for you. It is best to eat plenty of protein, fat, and carbs at each meal.

You may want to avoid eating plans such as intermittent fasting. This eating plan can be useful for weight loss and other benefits but can make it much harder to eat enough calories to gain weight.

Make sure to eat at least three meals per day and try to add energy-dense snacks whenever possible.

Increase your intake of energy-dense foods

It's very important to eat mostly whole foods, like fruits, vegetables, whole grains, and legumes.

However, these foods tend to be more filling than processed junk foods, making it harder to get in enough calories.

Using plenty of spices, sauces, and condiments can help with this. The tastier your food is, the easier it may be to eat a lot of it. Toppings may also add additional calories.

Also, try to emphasize energy-dense foods as much as possible. These are foods that contain many calories relative to their weight.

Here are some energy-dense foods that may help you gain weight:

• Nuts like almonds, walnuts, macadamia nuts, and peanuts

• Dried fruit, including raisins, dates, prunes, and others

• High fat dairy, such as whole milk, full-fat yogurt, cheese, and cream

• Fats and oils like extra virgin olive oil and avocado oil

• Grains, including whole grains like oats and brown rice

- Meat, such as chicken, beef, pork, and lamb; you can also choose fattier cuts

- Tubers, including potatoes, sweet potatoes, and yams

- Other energy-dense foods like dark chocolate, avocados, peanut butter, coconut milk, granola, and trail mix

It may be a good idea to avoid over-consuming vegetables and fruit if gaining weight is a priority for you. The fiber in fruits and vegetables can lead you to feeling full faster. This can leave less room for energy-dense foods.

If you need more suggestions, these healthy foods may help you gain weight faster.

10 quick tips

Combining a high calorie intake with heavy resistance training may help you gain weight.

That being said, there are several other strategies to gain weight even faster.

Here are 10 additional tips for gaining weight:

1. Avoid drinking water before meals. This can fill your stomach and make it harder to get in enough calories.

2. Eat more often. Squeeze in an additional meal or snack whenever you can, such as before bed.

3. Drink milk. Drinking whole milk to quench thirst can be a simple way to

get in more high-quality protein and calories.

4. Try weight gainer shakes. If you are having trouble gaining weight, consider weight gainer shakes. These are very high in protein, carbs, and calories.

5. Use bigger plates. Consider using large plates if you're trying to get in more calories, as smaller plates can cause people to eat less.

6. Add cream to your coffee. This is a simple way to add in more calories.

7. Take creatine. The muscle-building supplement creatine monohydrate can help you gain a few pounds in muscle weight.

8. Get quality sleep. Sleeping properly is very important for muscle growth.

9. Eat your protein and fat source first. If you have a mix of foods on your plate, eat the calorie-dense and protein-rich foods first. Eat higher fiber foods like raw vegetables last.

10. Avoid smoking, and if you smoke, consider quitting. Smokers tend to weigh less than non-smokers, and quitting smoking often leads to weight gain.

HOW CAN I GAIN WEIGHT WITHOUT EATING TOO MUCH?

To gain weight, you'll likely need to consume additional calories.

You can avoid overeating too much and make sure that the excess calories go to your muscles instead of just your fat cells by starting a resistance training program.

Resistance training, or strength training, includes both bodyweight exercises and free weights. Resistance training leads to muscle hypertrophy, which increases muscle mass.

Combining protein supplementation with resistance training can promote additional gains in lean body mass beyond those gained by resistance exercise alone.

One study found that protein supplementation during resistance training for six weeks increased lean mass growth by 27% in healthy adults.

If you're completely out of shape or new to training, consider hiring a qualified personal trainer or taking a class to help you get started, if this is possible for you.

You may also want to consult with a doctor if you have skeletal problems or any medical issues.

To maximize muscle mass, it's best to focus on resistance training over cardio.

Doing some cardio can help improve fitness and well-being, but you may want to avoid doing so much that you end up burning all the additional calories you're eating.

How long will it take to gain weight?

By consuming 500 additional calories a day, a person might gain an average of about 15 pounds (6.8 kg) over 6 months.

A more aggressive approach of consuming an additional 1,000 calories per day may allow a weight gain of about 25 pounds (11.4 kg) over 6 months. However, a large portion of this weight gain may be compromised of fat.

It can be very difficult for some people to gain weight, and the amount of time it takes to gain weight will be different for everyone.

That may be because your body might have a certain weight, called a setpoint, where it feels comfortable. It's theorized that whether you try to go under your setpoint (lose weight) or over it (gain weight), your body resists changes by regulating your hunger levels and metabolic rate.

When you eat more calories and gain weight, your body may respond by reducing your appetite and boosting your metabolism. This may be largely mediated by your brain, as well as weight-regulating hormones like leptin.

However, researchers have not proven or dismissed their theory and more research is still needed.

So you may encounter a certain level of difficulty.

Reasons You May Be Gaining Weight Unintentionally

1. You eat too many highly processed foods

Many healthy foods, such as oats, frozen fruit, and yogurt, are minimally processed.

However, highly processed foods, including sugary cereals, fast food, and microwave dinners, pack a slew of harmful ingredients, as well as added sugars, preservatives, and unhealthy fats.

What's more, numerous studies link highly processed food to weight gain, in addition to rising obesity rates in the United States and around the world.

For example, a 2019 study in 19,363 Canadian adults found that those who ate the most ultra-processed foods were 32% more likely to be obese than those who ate the least.

Highly processed foods are typically packed with calories yet devoid of essential nutrients, such as protein and fiber, which keep you feeling full.

In fact, in a 2-week study in 20 people, participants ate about 500 more calories per day on an ultra-processed diet than on an unprocessed diet.

Thus, you should consider cutting out processed meals and snacks, focusing instead on whole foods.

2. You eat too much sugar

Regularly downing sugary foods and beverages, such as candy, cakes, soda, sports drinks, ice cream, iced tea, and sweetened coffee drinks, can easily enlarge your waistline.

Many studies link sugar intake not only to weight gain but also an increased risk of chronic health conditions, including type 2 diabetes and heart disease.

In particular, sugary beverages are the largest source of added sugar in the United States and strongly associated with weight gain.

For instance, a review of 30 studies in 242,352 children and adults tied sweetened beverage intake to weight gain and obesity.

You can try gradually reducing your sugar intake to ease the process.

3. You have a sedentary lifestyle

Inactivity is a common contributor to weight gain and chronic diseases.

Working a desk job, watching TV, driving, and using a computer or phone are all sedentary activities.

A study in 464 people with obesity and excess weight found that their average daily sitting time was 6.2 hours on working days and 6 hours on non-working days.

Work-related tasks were the largest contributor, followed by watching TV.

Making a few simple lifestyle changes, such as exercising and sitting less, can make a big difference.

For example, a 3-month study in 317 workers found that replacing just 1 hour of sitting with 1 hour of standing during the workday reduced total fat mass and waist circumference while increasing lean muscle mass.

Research has also shown that engaging in excessive screen time contributes significantly to unintentional weight gain.

Even small adjustments, such as taking a walk after dinner instead of watching TV, working out or walking during your lunch break, investing in a standing or treadmill desk, or riding your bike to work, can counter weight gain.

4. You engage in yo-yo dieting

Yo-yo dieting refers to cycles of intentional weight loss followed by unintentional weight regain.

Notably, this pattern is linked to an increased risk of weight gain over time.

In a study in 2,785 people, those who had dieted within the previous year had greater body weights and waist circumferences than those of non-dieters. Other studies reveal that restrictive eating and dieting may lead to future weight gain due to your body's physiological responses to such behaviors, such as changes in hunger and fullness hormones.

Plus, most people who lose weight through restrictive dieting gain back most or all of it within 5 years.

To keep weight off long term, you should focus on sustainable lifestyle changes. These include exercise, cutting out processed and sugary foods, and eating nutrient-dense, whole foods rich in fiber and protein.

5. You have an undiagnosed medical issue

Although many lifestyle factors contribute to unintentional weight gain, certain medical conditions may also play a role. These include:

- Hypothyroidism. This condition affects your thyroid gland and may cause weight gain or difficulty with weight loss.

- Depression. This common mental condition is linked to weight gain and obesity.

- Polycystic ovary syndrome (PCOS). PCOS is marked by hormonal imbalances that affect women of reproductive age. It may cause weight gain and make it difficult to lose weight.

- Binge eating disorder (BED). BED is categorized by recurrent episodes of uncontrollable overeating and can lead to many health complications, including weight gain.

Other conditions, such as diabetes and Cushing's syndrome, are likewise associated with weight gain, so it's important to get the right diagnosis from your medical practitioner.

What's more, certain medications, including antidepressant and antipsychotic drugs, can lead to weight gain. Speak to a health professional if you believe you're gaining weight due to your medicine.

6. You don't get enough sleep

Sleep is essential for overall health and well-being. Insufficient sleep may trigger weight gain, among other negative effects. A study in 92 women demonstrated that those who slept fewer than 6 hours daily had the highest body mass index (BMI) and the highest levels of visfatin (a protein secreted by fat cells), compared with women who slept 6 hours or more per day.

In a 2-week study in 10 adults with excess weight following a low-calorie diet, those who slept 5.5 hours per night lost 55% less body fat and 60% more muscle mass than those who slept 8.5 hours per night.

As such, increasing your sleep time may aid weight loss.

Some evidence associates 7 or more hours of sleep per night with a 33% greater likelihood of weight loss, compared with sleeping fewer than 7 hours.

If you have poor sleep quality, you can try limiting screen time before bed, reducing your caffeine intake, and going to sleep at a consistent time.

7. You don't eat enough whole foods

If you regularly eat processed foods, switching to a diet that's higher in whole foods is an easy and effective way to promote weight loss and improve many other aspects of your health.

In fact, the most important factor in weight loss is choosing whole, minimally processed foods.

One study divided 609 adults with excess weight into groups that followed either a low-fat or low-carb diet for 12 months.

Both groups were instructed to maximize their vegetable intake, restrict their intake of added sugars, trans fats, and refined carbohydrates, eat mostly whole, minimally processed, nutrient-dense foods, and prepare most meals at home.

The study found that people in both diet groups lost similar amounts of weight 12 pounds (5.4 kg) for the low-fat group and 13 pounds (5.9 kg) for the low-carb group. This demonstrated that diet quality, not macronutrient content, was the most important factor in their weight loss.

Incorporating whole foods into your diet doesn't have to be difficult. Start by slowly adding more nutrient-dense whole foods, such as vegetables, fruits, beans, eggs, nuts, and seeds, into your meals and snacks.

8. You're stressed out

Chronic stress is a common problem that can affect your weight.

High levels of the stress hormone cortisol have been shown to increase hunger and your desire for highly palatable, calorie-dense foods, which can cause weight gain.

What's more, studies indicate that people with obesity have higher cortisol levels than those without this condition.

Interestingly, stress management may promote weight loss.

In an 8-week study in 45 adults with obesity, those who engaged in relaxation techniques like deep breathing lost significantly more weight than those who only received standard dietary advice.

To reduce stress, try incorporating evidence-based relaxation practices into your routine. These include yoga, spending time in nature, and meditation.

9. You eat too many calories

Overeating remains a prominent cause of weight gain.

If you take in more calories than you burn per day, you'll likely gain weight.

Mindless eating, frequent snacking, and making calorie-rich, nutrient-poor dietary choices all promote excessive calorie intake.

It can be difficult to determine your calorie needs on your own, so consult a registered dietitian if you struggle with overeating.

Some simple ways to avoid overeating include paying attention to hunger and fullness cues by eating mindfully, following a high-fiber, high-protein diet rich in plant foods, drinking water instead of calorie-rich beverages, and increasing your activity level.

WEIGHT GAIN SMOOTHIE

RECIPES

Here are some smoothie recipes you can try for weight gain, each of these recipes have high tendency of making you gain weight, each one of these recipes are explained by listing the ingredients alongside the instruction on preparation;

1. Peanut Butter Avocado Smoothie for Weight Gain

EQUIPMENT

Knife

Food Processor

Large-Width Straws

Ingredients

• 6 Medjool dates, pitted and chopped (fresh dates, not the ones in the baking aisle)

• 6 tablespoons boiling water

• 1¼ cups frozen chopped avocado

• 4 tablespoons creamy peanut butter

• 2 cups milk, 2%

• ½ teaspoon cinnamon

• 2 tablespoons dark cocoa powder

• chopped peanuts, whipped cream, maraschino cherries (optional toppings)

Instructions

• Pour the boiling water over the Medjool dates. Let sit for 10 minutes.

- Put the dates and water into a food processor and blend into a smooth date paste. You will need to scrape down the sides of the processor with a spatula several times because the dates will stick to the sides.

2. Pineapple smoothie

Ingredients

- 1 cup liquid of your choice (almond milk, water, coconut water, soy milk)

- 1 serving vanilla protein powder

- 1 cup diced, pineapple

- 1/2 banana (optional)

- 1 tablespoon chia seeds (optional)

- 2 cups ice (more if you like it frothy)

Instructions

• Put all ingredients in a blender and pulse until your reach you desired consistency. Add more ice if needed.

3. Strawberry Banana Orange Power Smoothie

Ingredients

• 2 cups frozen strawberries

• 1 large orange

• 1 large banana

• 1/4 cup plain Greek yogurt or other vegan substitute

• 1 1/2 cups orange juice, water, almond milk, or other liquid of your choice.

Instructions

1. Add all the ingredients to your blender and blend until smooth.

2. Enjoy!

4. Blueberry Coconut Water Smoothie (With Hemp Hearts)

Ingredients

- 1 ½ cups frozen blueberries

- 1 cup coconut water

- ½ cup yogurt full-fat plain or greek

- ¼ teaspoon coconut extract

- 1 tablespoon hemp hearts

Instructions

1. Combine all ingredients in the blender and blend until smooth.

5. Spinach Banana Smoothie

Equipment

• Blender

Ingredients

• 1 medium banana

• 1 big handful spinach (1 handful = approx. 60g)

• 1 tbsp peanut butter

• 1¼ cup unsweetened soy milk (or your fave milk – almond, oat, coconut, even water)

Instructions

1. Easy as hell – throw everything together!

2. And blend!

6. Keto Blueberry Smoothie

Ingredients

• 1 cup blueberries frozen

• 1 cup milk of choice I used unsweetened coconut milk

• 2 tablespoon almond butter

• 1 tablespoon granulated sweetener of choice optional

Instructions

1. In a high speed blender, add all your ingredients and blend until thick and creamy.

2. Pour into two glasses and serve immediately.

7. Keto Smoothie (3 Ingredients!)

Ingredients

• 1 cup milk of choice

• 1/2 cup sugar free condensed milk can use Greek yogurt

• 2 cups ice crushed

• 1 cup frozen strawberries

Instructions

1. In a high speed blender, add your milk, condensed milk (or Greek yogurt), and ice, and blend until combined. Add the strawberries and blend until the desired texture is achieved.

2. Pour the smoothie into four glasses and enjoy it immediately.

8. Blueberry Chia Smoothie

Equipment

- Blender

Ingredients

- ½ cup milk

- ½ cup Greek yogurt or any probiotic yogurt

- 1 cup blueberries frozen

- 1 banana

- 1 tablespoon chia seeds

- 1 teaspoon Ceylon Cinnamon

- Sweetener (optional): honey, or maple syrup

Instructions

1. Add all ingredients in the blender. Note: add wet ingredients first for easier blending.

2. Mix everything at high speed until you get a smooth silky texture.

3. If the smoothie is too thick, add a little more liquid – milk or water. Blend again until everything is well combined.

4. Taste the smoothie and add additional sweetener if the smoothie is not sweet enough to your taste.

5. Transfer the smoothie into a smoothie glass.

6. Add toppings if desired. Be creative.

7. Serve and enjoy!

9. Peaches and Cream Oatmeal Smoothie

Equipment

• Blendtec Blender

Ingredients

• 1 cup almond milk with honey

• 1/4 cup rolled oats

• 1/4 cup honey greek yogurt

• 3/4 cup frozen peaches

Instructions

1. Combine all the ingredients in a blender.

2. Pulse until peaches are blended in well.

3. Calories: 240.

10. Orange avocado smoothie

Ingredients:

- 1/2 ripe banana, frozen

- 1 orange (or two clementines), peeled

- 1/2 ripe avocado

- 1 cup baby spinach leaves

- 1 and 1/2 cups unsweetened vanilla almond milk

Instructions

Place all of the ingredients in a blender and blend until smooth.

11. Banana, Coffee + Almond Butter Smoothie

Equipment

Blender

Ingredients

• 1 cup cold brew or strong leftover coffee, cooled

• 1 banana

• 2 Tablespoon almond butter or nut butter of choice

• 1/3 cup coconut milk

• 1.5 cup ice

Instructions

1. Add all ingredients to a high speed blender.

Blend on high until fully combined and all the ingredients are broken down. Serve immediately.

2. 1 banana frozen

3. 2 cups baby spinach raw

Instructions

1.Place all ingredients in a blender and blend until smooth. Add ice for a thicker smoothie.

12. Banana Cashew Butter Chia Seed Smoothie

Ingredients

- 1/4 cup cashew butter

- 2 frozen medium bananas

- 1 cup unsweetened almond milk

- 1 tsp cinnamon

- 2 Tbsp chia seeds

- toppings of choice (optional)

Instructions

1. Blend everything together and enjoy!

13. Tropical Breakfast Smoothie

Ingredients

- 1 cup vanilla almond milk

- 2 rounded scoops of Orgain Sweet Vanilla Bean Protein Powder

- 1 banana

- 1 handful frozen strawberries

- 1 handful frozen mango slices

Instructions

1. Combine all ingredients in blender and blend until smooth. Drink immediately or store in fridge for up to 24 hours.

14. Coconut Pineapple Orange Smoothie

Ingredients

- 2 oranges

- 1 banana

- 1/3 cup pineapple (fresh is best, but canned works)

- 1/4 cup yogurt

- 1/3 cup milk (this would be amazing with coconut milk!)

Instructions

1. Blend until smooth.

2. Sprinkle with coconut and/or orange zest.

15. Clementine Avocado Smoothie

Ingredients

• 2 clementines, peeled

• 1 ripe avocado, pitted and scooped from the peel

• 1 ripe banana, peeled

• 1 cup unsweetened animal or plant-based milk

• 2 cups fresh baby spinach

• 1 tablespoon honey, optional

• Handful of ice

Instructions

1. Combine all ingredients, including the honey, if using, in the basin of a blender.

Blend on high until very smooth and creamy. Pour into two glasses and enjoy.

16. Keto Kale & Coconut Shake Recipe (No added fruit or sugar)

Ingredients

1 cup unsweetened almond milk (substitute your favourite non-dairy milk)

1/2 cup full-fat canned coconut milk

4 cups chopped kale (you can also do a mix of spinach & kale)

1/4 cup ground coconut (unsweetened)

1 1-inch piece fresh ginger, peeled (optional--skip it if you don't like the taste of ginger)

1/4 teaspoon kosher salt (or Celtic sea salt if you have it--it's rich in beneficial minerals!)

1 cup ice

Instructions

Pour almond and coconut milk into base of blender, followed by ginger, kale, ground coconut, salt, and ice.

Puree until very smooth. (I have a professional style Ninja blender so this only takes 1 minute for me, but with a standard blender you may need to let this go about 3-5 minutes.)

17. Banana Avocado Green Smoothie

Equipment

• Blender

Ingredients

- 2 Bananas

- 1 cup Frozen Avocado

- 1 cup Packed Spinach

- 3 Pitted Dates

- 1 tbsp Ground Chia Seed

- 1 cup Unsweetened Coconut Milk

- 2 cups Coconut Water

- 1 cup Crushed Ice

Instructions

1. I like to start by putting all dry ingredients in the blender first. Place 2 peeled, ripe bananas in blender. Add 1 cup frozen, diced avocado, 1 cup packed spinach, 3 pitted dates, 1 tbsp ground chia seed.

2. Next, add 1 cup unsweetened coconut milk and 2 cups coconut water. Put lid on blender and blend until smooth.

3. Add up to 1 cup crushed ice to blender and blend to get your desired consistency.

4. Pour smoothie and enjoy!

18. Healthy Carrot Cake Smoothie

Ingredients:

- 1 cup almond milk

- 1/2 cup Greek yogurt

- 1/3 cup walnuts

- 1 banana

- 1 cup carrots (chopped)

- 1/4 tsp fresh ginger (grated)

- 1 tsp cinnamon

- a pinch of nutmeg

- 1 tsp vanilla extract

Instructions

1. Pop all the ingredients into a blender.

2. Add some ice if needed and blend!

19. Coconut Almond Spinach Smoothie

Ingredients:

- 1 cup of canned coconut milk

- 1 banana

- 2 tbsp almond butter

- 2 tbsp pumpkin seeds

- 2 cups spinach

- ½ tsp vanilla extract

- ½ cup ice cubes

Instructions

1. Pop all the ingredients into a blender.

2. Add some ice if needed and blend!

20. Blueberry Protein Smoothie

Ingredients:

- 2 cups of blueberries

- 1/2 cup oat milk

- 1/2 cup spinach

- 1/2 banana

- 1 tbsp vanilla protein powder

- 1/2 cup greek yogurt

- 1/2 cup rolled oats

Instructions

1. Pop all the ingredients into a blender.

2. Add some ice if needed and blend!

21. Coffee Protein Smoothie

Ingredients:

• 1/2 cup brewed coffee (cooled down)

• 1 large banana

• 2 tbsp unsweetened peanut butter

• 2 tbsp vanilla protein powder

• 1 tbsp cocoa powder

• 1 cup coconut milk

• 1/2 cup ice cubes

Instructions

1. Pop all the ingredients into a blender.

2. Add some ice if needed and blend!

22. Pineapple Banana Smoothie

Ingredients:

- 1 banana

- 1 1/2 cups pineapple chunks (fresh or frozen)

- 1/2 cup rolled oats

- 1 tbsp chia seeds

- 1/4 cup white beans (canned)

- 1 cup soy milk

Instructions

1. Pop all the ingredients into a blender.

2. Add some ice if needed and blend!

23. Banana Cinnamon Oatmeal Smoothie

Ingredients

- 1 cup unsweetened almond milk

- 1 tbsp almond butter

- 1 large banana

- 5-6 ice cubes

- 1/4 cup rolled oats

- 1 tsp vanilla extract

- 2 tbsp vanilla protein powder

- 1 tsp cinnamon

- 1 tbsp ground flaxseed

- 1 tbsp honey

Instructions

1. Pop all the ingredients into a blender.

2. Add some ice if needed and blend!

24. Chocolate Avocado Smoothie

Ingredients:

- 1 1/2 cup soy milk

- 1 banana

- 1/2 avocado

- 1 cup spinach

- 2 tbsp cocoa powder

- 1 tbsp honey

- 1 tbsp hemp seeds

- 1 tsp cinnamon

- a pinch of nutmeg

- a pinch of salt

Instructions

1. Pop all the ingredients into a blender.

2. Add some ice if needed and blend!

25. Orange Coconut Protein Smoothie

Ingredients:

- 1 cup orange juice

- 1/2 cup coconut milk

- 3 tbsp vanilla protein powder

- 1 banana

- 1/2 avocado

- 1/2 cup ice

- 1/2 tsp orange zest

Instructions

1. Pop all the ingredients into a blender.

2. Add some ice if needed and blend!

26. Blackberry Raspberry Smoothie

Ingredients:

- 1 cup blackberries (frozen)

- 1/2 cup raspberries (frozen)

- 1/2 avocado

- 1/2 cup Greek yogurt

- 1 cup oat milk

- 1 tbsp honey

- 1/2 tsp vanilla extract

Instructions

1. Pop all the ingredients into a blender.

2. Add some ice if needed and blend!

27. Strawberry Peanut Butter Smoothie

Ingredients:

- 3/4 cup plain yogurt

- 1 cup strawberries (frozen)

- 1 banana

- 3 tbsp unsweetened peanut butter

- 2 tbsp milk

Instructions

1. Pop all the ingredients into a blender.

2. Add some ice if needed and blend!

28. Green spirulina smoothie

Ingredients

- ½ small avocado, peeled and stoned

- 1 tsp spirulina powder

- 50g baby spinach

- ¼ cucumber, roughly chopped

- 1 lime, zested and juiced

- 10g mint, plus a sprig to garnish

- 75ml apple juice (not from concentrate), chilled

- 1 tsp honey (optional)

Instructions

Tip all the ingredients into a blender or food processor with 75ml cold water, and blitz until smooth. Or, put everything in a bowl and blitz with a hand blender.

Pour into a tall glass and garnish with a mint sprig, if you like. Drink straightaway.

29. Strawberry green goddess smoothie

Ingredients

- 160g ripe strawberries, hulled

- 160g baby spinach

- 1 small avocado, halved and the flesh scooped out

- 150ml pot bio yogurt

- 2 small oranges, juiced, plus ½ tsp finely grated zest

Instructions

Put all the ingredients in a blender and whizz until completely smooth. If it's a little thick, add a drop of chilled water then blitz again. Pour into glasses and drink straight away.

30. Peanut butter smoothie

Ingredients

- 200ml oat milk

- 1 banana, peeled and chopped

- 20g peanut butter

- 1 tbsp rolled oats

- pinch of cinnamon

- pinch of allspice

- pinch of nutmeg (optional)

- small handful ice cubes

Instructions

Whizz all the ingredients together in a blender (one suitable for crushing ice) until smooth. Pour into a tall glass and serve.

31. Banana smoothie

Ingredients

- 500ml unsweetened almond milk

- 2 tbsp almond butter

- 6 prunes

- 1 tsp cinnamon

- 1 small ripe banana

Instructions

In a blender, whizz the almond milk with the almond butter, prunes, cinnamon and banana.

Transfer to 2 bottles and chill until ready to drink, or pack for lunch on the go. The smoothies will keep in the fridge for 2 days.

32. Mango lassi

Ingredients

• 3-4 ripe mangoes (honey mangoes if possible)

• 500g natural yogurt

• a pinch ground cardamom (crush the seeds from 1-2 pods)

• 1 tbsp honey

• 2 limes juiced, to taste

Instructions

Put all the ingredients apart from the lime juice in a food processor and blitz.

Add the lime juice along with a pinch of salt, to taste, if the cardamom isn't strong enough then add a little more, then pour into glasses with some ice cubes and serve.

33. Cherry smoothie

Ingredients

- 300g frozen or fresh cherries pitted

- 150g natural yogurt

- 1 large banana sliced

- ½ tsp vanilla extract

Instructions

Tip all the ingredients into a blender and blitz until smooth. Adjust the thickness to your liking with 50-100ml cold water.

Serve in four glasses or chill for up to 24 hrs, giving a good stir before serving.

34. Green breakfast smoothie

Ingredients

- 1 handful spinach (about 50g/2oz), roughly chopped

- 100g broccoli florets, roughly chopped

- 2 celery sticks

- 4 tbsp desiccated coconut

- 1 banana

- 300ml rice milk (good dairy alternative - we used one from Rude Health)

- ¼ tsp spirulina or 1 scoop of greens powder or vegan protein powder (optional)

Instructions

Whizz 300ml water and the ingredients in a blender until smooth.

35. Blueberry & banana power smoothie

Ingredients

- 2 ripe bananas peeled

- 125g blueberries (fresh or frozen)

- 300g pack silken tofu, drained

- 2 tbsp porridge oats

Instructions

Whizz all of the ingredients together in a blender with 300ml water.

Drink straight away or transfer to a bottle for later, shaking well before drinking.

36. Avocado smoothie

Ingredients

- ½ avocado, peeled, stoned and roughly chopped
- generous handful spinach
- generous handful kale, washed well
- 50g pineapple chunks
- 10cm piece cucumber, roughly chopped
- 300ml coconut water

Instructions

Put the avocado, spinach, kale, pineapple and cucumber in the blender.

Top up with coconut water, then blitz until smooth.

37. Avocado & strawberry smoothie

Ingredients

- ½ avocado stoned, peeled and cut into chunks

- 150g strawberry, halved

- 4 tbsp low-fat natural yogurt

- 200ml semi-skimmed milk

- lemon or lime juice to taste

- honey to taste

Instructions

Put all the ingredients in a blender and whizz until smooth. If the consistency is too thick, add a little water.

38. Green rainbow smoothie bowl

Ingredients

- 50g spinach

- 1 avocado stoned, peeled and halved

- 1 ripe mango stoned, peeled and cut into chunks

- 1 apple cored and cut into chunks

- 200ml almond milk

- 1 dragon fruit peeled and cut into even chunks

- 100g mixed berries (we used strawberries, raspberries and blueberries)

Instructions

Put the spinach, avocado, mango, apple and almond milk in a blender, and blitz until smooth and thick. Divide between two bowls and top with the dragon fruit and berries.

39. Strawberry & banana almond smoothie

Ingredients

- 1 small banana

- 7 strawberries hulled

- 3 tbsp 0% bio-yogurt

- 3 tbsp skimmed milk

- 2 tbsp ground almond

Instructions

Slice the banana into the bowl of a food processor, or a jug if using a hand blender. Add the strawberries, yogurt, milk and ground almonds, and blitz until completely smooth. Pour into a glass and enjoy.

40. Breakfast smoothie

Ingredients

- 1 small ripe banana

- about 140g blackberries, blueberries, raspberries or strawberries (or use a mix), plus extra to serve

- apple juice or mineral water, optional

- runny honey to serve

Instructions

Slice the banana into your blender or food processor and add the berries of your choice. Whizz until smooth. With the blades whirring, pour in juice or water to make the consistency you like. Toss a few extra fruits on top, drizzle with honey and serve.

41. Mango & banana smoothie

Ingredients

- 1 medium mango

- 1 banana

- 500ml orange juice

- 4 ice cubes

Instructions

Cut the mango down either side of the flat stone, then peel and cut the flesh into chunks.

Peel and chop the banana.

Put all the ingredients into a food processor or blender, then process until smooth and thick. Keep in the fridge and use the day you make it.

42. Cranberry & raspberry smoothie

Ingredients

• 200ml cranberry juice

• 175g frozen raspberry defrosted

• 100ml milk

• 200ml natural yogurt

- 1 tbsp caster sugar or to taste

- mint sprigs, to serve

Instructions

Place all the ingredients into a blender and pulse until smooth. Pour into glasses and serve topped with fresh mint.

43. Blueberry & banana power smoothie

Ingredients

- 2 ripe bananas peeled

- 125g blueberries (fresh or frozen)

- 300g pack silken tofu drained

- 2 tbsp porridge oats

Instructions

Whizz all of the ingredients together in a blender with 300ml water. Drink straight away or transfer to a bottle for later, shaking well before drinking.

44. Peach Melba smoothie

Ingredients

- 410g can peach halves

- 100g frozen raspberry plus a few for garnish

- 100ml orange juice

- 150ml fresh custard, plus a spoonful for garnish

Instructions

Drain and rinse peaches and place in a blender with raspberries.

Add orange juice and fresh custard and whizz together.

Pour over ice, garnish with another spoonful of custard and a few raspberries. Best served chilled.

45. Creamy mango & coconut smoothie

Ingredients

- 200ml (½ tall glass) coconut milk (we used Kara Dairy Free)

- 4 tbsp coconut milk yogurt (we used Coyo)

- 1 banana

- 1 tbsp ground flaxseed, sunflower and pumpkin seed (we used Linwoods)

- 120g (¼ bag) frozen mango chunks

- 1 passion fruit to finish (optional)

Instructions

Measure all the ingredients or use a tall glass for speed – they don't have to be exact. Put them into a blender and blitz until smooth. Pour into 1 tall glass (you'll have enough for a top up) or two short tumblers. Cut the passion fruit in half, if using, and scrape the seeds on top.

46. Turmeric smoothie bowl

Ingredients

- 10cm/4in fresh turmeric, or 2 tsp ground turmeric

- 3 tbsp coconut milk yogurt (we used Co Yo), or the cream skimmed from the top of canned coconut milk

- 50g gluten-free oats

- 1 tbsp cashew butter (or a handful of cashews)

- 2 bananas peeled and roughly chopped

- ½ tsp ground cinnamon

- 1 tbsp chia seeds or chopped nuts, to serve

Instructions

Peel the turmeric root, if using, and grate. Put all ingredients in a blender with 600ml water and blend until smooth. Serve in a bowl with chia seeds or some chopped nuts sprinkled over.

CONCLUSION

There are many reasons for wanting to gain weight.

It's important to do so by eating nutritionally-dense foods and building lean muscle mass.

At the end of the day, changing your weight is a marathon, not a sprint. It can take a long time, and you need to be consistent if you want to succeed in the long run.

If you're struggling to gain weight despite trying the strategies discussed above, it's important to talk with a doctor or dietitian. A dietitian can help you employ eating strategies that may help you reach your goal.

Many factors can contribute to unintentional weight gain.

Poor sleep, sedentary activities, and eating too many processed or sugary foods are just some of the habits that may increase your risk of weight gain.

Printed in Great Britain
by Amazon

13980316R00068